How to use this book

This quirky and funny story tells us, in both rhyming English and using signs taken directly from British Sign Language, about a visit to the zoo by a little girl and her daddy.

The story can be enjoyed by itself or as a fun and easy way of learning sign language.

As you read the story some words are highlighted in either red or blue.

All the words that are written in red can be signed as you read the story. For example, at the start of the story the word "Gorilla" is highlighted in red and can be signed.

Each page has photographs of children demonstrating the signs. To learn how to sign a particular word, simply look at the photographs and follow the simple instructions.

As the story progresses, the signs that you have learnt on previous pages appear in blue, whilst new signs are highlighted in red.

On each page of the book you are learning a new sign and by the end of the story you will have learnt twenty signs!

Using this simple method you will soon build up a vocabulary of signs sourced directly from British Sign Language whilst enjoying a really fun story!

This book really is the fun way to learn sign language!

Happy signing!

We went to the animal park today,
to see what the animals had to say.

"Look Daddy! A gorilla,
please can we chat?"

"Hmmph!"

"If that gorilla can talk
then I'll eat my hat!"

Animal (s)
With claw shaped hands and palms facing downwards,
make small forward movements as though creeping
through the jungle.

Gorilla
Beat your chest with your fists, like a gorilla.

3

We went to the animal **park** today,
to see what the animals had to say.

"Look Daddy! A **lion**,
please can we chat?"

"Hmmph!"

"If that **lion** can talk
then I'll eat my hat!"

Park
With right hand 'flat' and palm facing downwards,
the thumb taps twice against the opposite shoulder.

Lion
With both hands in a 'claw' like shape, mime the mane of a male lion around your head.

We went to the animal park today,
to see what the animals had to say.

"Look Daddy! A giraffe,
please can we chat?"

"Hmmph!"

"If that giraffe can talk
then I'll eat my hat!"

See / Look
The index and middle fingers in a 'V' shape, move forward and away
from the eye.

Giraffe
With head tilted back slightly, mime the length of a giraffe's neck by moving a cupped hand up your neck towards your chin.

We went to the animal park today, to see what the animals had to say.

"Look Daddy! A snake please can we chat?"

"Hmmph!"

"If that snake can talk then I'll eat my hat!"

Daddy / Dad
With Index and middle fingers extended and together on both hands, the righthand fingers tap the back of the left index and middle fingers twice.

Snake

Hold your hand in a fist at your mouth with your knuckles facing forward, then flick your index and middle fingers out in a 'V' shape to mimic a snake's forked tongue.

We went to the animal park today,
to see what the animals had to say.

"Look Daddy! An elephant,
please can we chat?"

"Hmmph!"

"If that elephant can talk
then I'll eat my hat!"

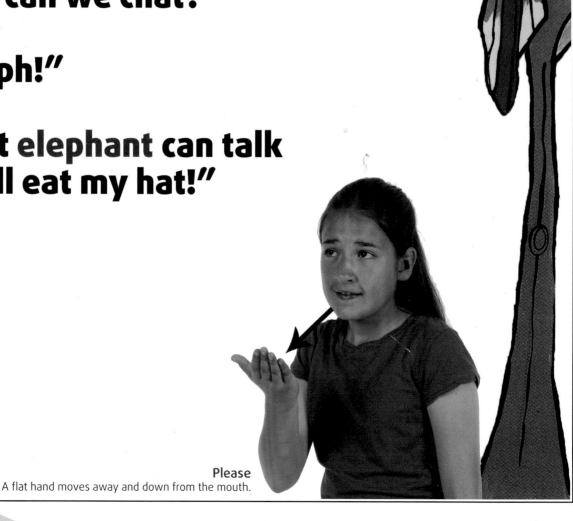

Please
A flat hand moves away and down from the mouth.

Elephant
The right hand forms the shape of a 'C' and mimes the shape of an elephant's trunk, starting with your hand at your nose and moving down and away.

We went to the animal park today,
to see what the animals had to say.

"Look Daddy! A crocodile,
please can we chat?"

"Hmmph!"

"If that crocodile can talk
then I'll eat my hat!"

Chat / Talk
The fingers of both hands open and close against the thumbs,
mimicking the movement of a mouth opening and closing.

Crocodile
With claw shaped hands and palms facing each other, extend your
arms and mime the opening and closing of a crocodile's mouth.

We went to the animal park today,
to see what the animals had to say.

"Look Daddy! A penguin,
please can we chat?"

"Hmmph!"

"If that penguin can talk
then I'll eat my hat!"

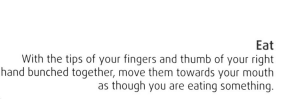

Eat
With the tips of your fingers and thumb of your right
hand bunched together, move them towards your mouth
as though you are eating something.

Penguin
With 'flat' hands held at your waist and palms facing downwards,
point your fingers away from your body and waddle like a penguin.

We went to the animal park today,
to see what the animals had to say.

"Look Daddy! A hippopotamus,
please can we chat?"

"Hmmph!"

"If that hippopotamus can talk
then I'll eat my hat!"

Hat
With the index fingers and thumbs of both hands touching each other,
mime pulling a hat onto your head.

Hippopotamus
Hold both fists in front of your body, with your knuckles facing each other, then mime the opening and closing of a Hippopotamus' mouth.

17

We went to the animal park today,
to see what the animals had to say.

"Look Daddy! A monkey,
please can we chat?"

"Wow! Look he can sign Dad,
now how cool is that!"

Sign
With both hands open and palms facing each other, slightly apart, rotate your hands forwards in small alternating circles, so that when one hand is up the other is down and visa versa.

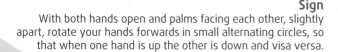

Monkey
Hands scratch under the arms like a monkey.

Cool

With the index finger and thumb held out in front of you in the shape of a 'C', move your hand to your right in an arc and then form the letter 'L' to show the first and last letters of 'Cool'.